Mania or Miracles?

The Gifts of Being

a

Manic-Depressive Personality

Veckie,
Thanks again for all your kindness through the many years of our friendship.
God Bless you,
Jim

James D. Raleigh, MDP
(Manic-Depressive Personality)

authorHOUSE™

1663 LIBERTY DRIVE, SUITE 200
BLOOMINGTON, INDIANA 47403
(800) 839-8640
WWW.AUTHORHOUSE.COM

First published by AuthorHouse 11/29/05

ISBN: 1-4208-8932-X (sc)

Library of Congress Control Number: 2005909362

Printed in the United States of America
Bloomington, Indiana

This book is printed on acid-free paper.

Cover design and interior illustrations by Sarah Kladzyk

This book is dedicated to my father, Ed.

"A quiet mind is not an idle gift ..." (ACIM)

How is this quiet found? No one can fail to find it who but seeks out its conditions. God's peace can never come where anger is, for anger must deny that peace exists. Who sees anger as justified in any way or any circumstance proclaims that peace is meaningless, and must believe that it cannot exist. In this condition, peace cannot be found. Therefore, forgiveness is the necessary condition for finding the peace of God. More than this, given forgiveness there (must) be peace. For what except attack will lead to war? And what but peace is opposite to war? Here the initial contrast stands out clear and apparent. Yet when peace is found, the war is meaningless. And it is conflict now that is perceived as nonexistent and unreal.

ACIM (*A Course in Miracles*) Manual for Teachers

Acknowledgments

I thank my children for always loving me, regardless of my mood swings.

Special thanks to General Motors Corporation for cooperating with me during my major manic attacks on company property.

I thank the many therapists and doctors who provided the help during my dark moods and frantic highs.

I thank my loving brothers and sisters for always taking me into their hearts and homes, regardless of the embarrassment to them because of my behavior.

I thank both my wives for understanding the illness and being accepting of me.

I thank Vera Hogan, who was instrumental in helping with the very first rough draft of the manuscript.

I thank Greg Raleigh, my son, for his input in editing this book, and Linda Lane Puryear, for the final editing and her friendship.

Jim Raleigh

Prologue

I write this message of love in fear that I am unworthy to share the joy and sorrows connected to the manic-depressive illness, something I have lived with since I first discovered its presence in my father.

My father, Ed, would invite me to his self-help groups, Recovery Inc., when I was fourteen years old and these self-help groups are still functioning today. The sorrows of my illness are overshadowed by the joy of self-restraint and a determined effort to conquer the apparent control the disease had over my peace of mind. The necessity to improve my awareness in order to allow the tablets of Lithium digested into my system on a daily basis has allowed me to increase my joy of living.

Life with my second wife, Frankie, allowed me the freedom to be me. Her love and encouragement afforded me the energy to overcome the fear of being accepted as an author. Frankie and I shared and witnessed much love in our lives, and this love gave us the wisdom to seek medical help. In Frankie's case, it was cancer. In mine, it was manic-depressive illness.

Frankie's encouragement that I should attempt to share my success story as a person who overcame the odds made me realize that the tendency is that the public only reads or hears of the unfortunate people who suffer from manic-depressive illness. Approximately 20 percent of the individuals who are stricken with the illness can function "beyond the cope" and live happy and productive lives. Additionally, it is disappointing to share that 20 percent choose to end their lives rather than live with their manic minds!

My story will reflect my mistakes (that I consider lessons) which allowed me to become aware of my true Self. This awareness keeps me in touch with the extensive mood swings that sometimes affect my sense of belonging in places that seem hostile and foreign; the sense of my true Self permits those mood swings to be balanced and modulated by true awareness of the choices available to me. This awareness has given me serenity. Through forgiveness, I continue to enjoy others, and myself. I am glad that my illness caused me to search within. Winning the battle has allowed me to forgive myself for not loving me more. I hope my story will allow you to do the same.

Table of Contents

Chapter One:
Manic-depressive Personality

Manic-depressive individuals are human beings who are considered to be mentally ill because of their inability to maintain consistent mood swings. Most human beings seem to be in a quest to obtain a mental state of joy or happiness. The definition of a mood swing is the relationship between mania (high) and depression (low). The exact causes of manic-depressive illness have not been determined.

The theories that surround the belief that the disease is hereditary cannot be proven because of the lack of consistency of the illnesses presence from one generation to another. The symptoms of the disorder are not disclosed in a pattern of behavior that is easily recognizable. For example, in my family, my father was a manic-depressive personality, while his six siblings had no signs of the illness. In my generation, I have six siblings, and my younger sister was stricken so severely with the disease of manic depression that she received social security insurance payments, because the illness disallowed her from being gainfully employed. I feel the stress from the illness caused her early death at fifty-three, from congestive heart failure. My other sisters and brothers have no apparent symptoms or concerns with the effects of being manic-depressive. Of my five offspring, two of my sons are manic-depressive. However, thanks to my father's good example of seeking help and the process of self-discovery of his illness, and through my sharing the good effects of Lithium and maintaining a balanced life, my two sons lead balanced and productive lives with a proper diet, a social balance, and proper sleep. Both are successes, not only in business careers, but with their marriages and family life, as well.

An exhaustive study of manic-depressive illness has been published, entitled *Manic-Depressive Illness*. Redman K. Goodwin and Kay Redfield Jameison's book is written in such a manner that laymen can understand both how the disease relates in our current social arena and the history of attempts to understand the mysteries behind this confusing mental illness. Case studies are reported in full detail with many testimonials from famous artists and other individuals that have worked through and around the swirling mind of the manic-depressive personality. The text also contains explicit explanations of all the various levels of mania and depression. In-depth studies are reported on the effects of Lithium and the benefits of using the drug to stabilize the mood swings related to manic-depressive illness.

There is no simple one-liner statement that can explain what may trigger the genes in a person's DNA to cause the manic-depressive illness to generate the manic highs and/or depression. One of the "triggers" that cause my mood swings is the change of the seasons. I noticed, in my late teens, that as the fall of the year approached I became withdrawn and had less enthusiasm for my daily chores around the house. My friends noticed I would become less talkative, and would ask if I felt okay. As winter closed in and the ice was on the lakes or ponds, you could find me skating next to an open fire at the shoreline, skimming across the ice in solitude, not wanting to be interrupted by anyone. As spring would approach and the buds were showing on the tree limbs, my mind would free itself from the chains of the winter. I would then pursue my simple, mundane duties with zest and optimism. The early summer months of May and June gave me enough freedom of thought, that I thought I could walk on water and touch the sun. My mind would race and my thoughts were full of total assurance that any goal I would attempt would be accomplished with ease!

A balanced human being with a stable mood swing pattern might be one considered to be consistent in his or her ability to maintain an even relationship between the two levels of joy and depression. The manic-depressive personality is generally aware of the out-of-balance mood swing activity, but will not attempt to adjust, or cannot change, their behavior to balance the mood swing variances.

This inconsistent relationship of swings causes various problems for the individual who is unaware of the benefits of a smooth mood swing cycle, similar to the sine wave curve that we graph to reflect the harmonics of a sound recorded in music.

I can relate to the erratic mood swing activity as I was diagnosed a manic-depressive personality in the fall of 1976. The mood swings during my first and most dramatic mania were more like the curve which is seen on a graph recording the heartbeat of a person suffering from cardiac arrest.

Manic-depressive mood swings are not simply controlled by drugs, electric shock treatments, or a combination of therapy with psychologists. They are also controlled through the realization of one's total relationship with their brain and the ability to select thoughts to change the thoughts that will eventually change their behaviors.

My views are from a layman's point of view and are not in agreement with the National Alliance of Mental Illness (NAMI). The NAMI describes the manic-depressive personality strictly from the aspects of the physical side of the person's being. For instance, the Diagnostic and Statistical Manual, 3rd edition, revised DSM-II-R classification for manic-depressive personality compares the behavior of the suspected MDP to an organic related list of physical symptoms developed from many investigative studies related to mental health. The symptoms of various levels of mood swings are listed in these tables. However, no consideration is given to the patient's mind/body connection. I differ with the NAMI's use of medications as an end solution in healing any mental disorder. Without healing the source of the disorder (your mind), no healing will ever occur. Granted, the organic brain must somehow be quieted long enough to wake the conscious mind of the manic-depressive personality's condition to allow their mind to gain control of the brain that requires truer guidance.

Manic-depressive illness can be healed or controlled, but only if the healing takes place in the mind of the individual who is cooperating with the chemicals that help control the disturbed brain during its mood swings. In my case of manic-depressive illness, lithium carbonate has worked very well.

The healing I speak of concerns itself with an individual's ability to recognize his or her own inner peace and "tap into that power" to allow more even mood swings. Very often, this requires moment-by-moment introspection. This healing is what I refer to as "beyond the cope." The Lithium, Prozac, therapy sessions, or whatever stabilizer is discovered for an individual is only the beginning of a good maintenance program for inner peace.

I was hospitalized many times in a mental hospital in southwestern Michigan, and it was not uncommon to be taken by the staff on field trips. During one of these field trips to a local shopping mall in Ann Arbor, Michigan I noticed a new book on a wire bookrack sitting in the open concourse of the mall. The title of the book caught my eye: *Love Is Letting Go of Fear* by Jerry Jampolsky. Rather than purchase the book (I had no cash), I quickly slipped the little paperback, with the picture of a ship and smiling face on the cover, into the vest pocket of my jacket. The book altered my life forever and has guided me to my inner peace.

Unaware that the source material for Jerry's book is taken from *A Course in Miracles,* I didn't fully understand how important the simple lessons that Dr. Jampolsky shares with us in his book. He completely interprets the *Course's* use of true forgiveness to undo the death-hold that we think the ego has on us through its use of guilt. I did not discover the full text of the *Course* until much later in life. Deepak Chopra and many other spiritual leaders had often quoted from the *Course* as I read their books. Finally, I started studying *A Course in Miracles* in 1992, and since have become a teacher/facilitator of the *Course.*

Chapter Two:

My Father's Gift to Me

My exposure to the manic mind began early in life. The anger and the loss of control that would overcome my parents in some family fights caused me nightmares, and polarized my love. After twenty years of exposure to the disease, I still don't know what causes bipolar activity, but I do know how to predict when it is going to occur in me.

My father, Ed, shared in his weekly self-help group meetings how spotting our emotions can help us ward off the anger that tips the scales in our behavior patterns. I was only fourteen when I first started to attend his group sessions, primarily to serve coffee and cookies. I also attended these meetings so I could begin to understand the man behind all this anger and hostility toward himself and his family members.

I first started to notice my father's anger through the resentment he shared during our talks while I was a young boy. I recall that, often, a disagreement would occur between my mother and him, and he would isolate himself to the garage. During the winter of 1959, it seemed that he and I spent nearly every evening sitting around an iron pot belly stove in the garage. He would pour his bourbon whiskey in a water glass and talk to me about his childhood and where he grew up in Ashland, Illinois.

His father, Ben, died when my father was only twelve years old. My father was forced to assume the role of father to his younger brothers and sisters. As he related his life to me, I recall the anger he felt towards the situation. He held unforgiving thoughts toward his mother. Later in his life, he shared with me that he had finally forgave his mother. Our talks made me aware of the results of not resolving our anger and what the denial of it can do to the love you truly want to express. The anger displayed physically between my parents crystallized a behavior in me. I have been fortunate to say that I have never used force to resolve my conflicts.

When I was asked if I would go along to the self-help group meetings to serve coffee, I couldn't say no. My fear and discomfort of going was overcome by the desire to find the answer to my dad's anger. The people in the groups would share their problems; sometimes they had been drinking too much, sometimes they would share their depressive episodes, and the list goes on. It didn't seem to matter what they were sharing; the act of verbalizing concerns with other people made an impact on me as a young man. The exchanges that occurred between people in these meetings resulted in their realization that they could teach themselves to be aware of their thoughts in order to control their actions before they acted on the fires of rage brewing in their minds.

The Recovery Inc. self-help groups my father facilitated on a weekly basis were held in a small office of the local grade school in Fenton, Michigan. Straight-backed chairs were formed in a circle prior to the meetings. I would make the coffee and place cookies and other baked goods on a plate for serving during the meetings. The size of the group rarely exceeded ten individuals. The meeting was low profile, with members stating their names and then voluntary reading from the Recovery Inc. text. My father would keep the members on the subject matter and offer his own personal story of the previous week and of how he had maintained his temper through the use of "spotting." He and others would relate whatever interactions that happened to them that caused their anger to get out of control.

The term *spotting* is taken from the Recovery Inc. text book on self-improvement. During the weekly meetings, my father demonstrated how this was developed. Basically, the individuals in the group are shown how it is possible to witness their thoughts just as their thoughts are occurring in times of anger or resentment towards another person. The term "spotting" came forth through the actual objective witnessing of their own individual behaviors, and then eventually the individual could "spot" their thoughts before the thoughts of anger got them into situations that caused loss of control of their emotions.

As I witnessed the individual's awareness to the benefits of "spotting," I began to realize the benefits of learning to control my thinking so that I could change my behaviors. The use of spotting has saved me from death and given me joy over the simplest things, like the cold, early morning dew on the grass and how the droplets of water hang in suspension as if frozen in space.

The many weekly meetings I attended with my father served to teach me the gift of being aware of my emotions before they took control over me. My foundation of self-awareness may have been taught in the weekly meetings I attended as a youth, but as you will read, I did not master it until my own personal "rock bottom" was hit.

There was more than the gift of spotting that my father passed along to me. He also gave me the genes of the manic-depressive personality. I resented that gift for many years until I stopped resisting the "present" and opened the package to find inside some very good attributes related to this disease.

Manic depression can cause untold pain, both physical and emotional, loss of companionship, major financial failures within our societies, and an unbelievable amount of lost time from the joys of the average human who maintains a flow between mood swings.

Chapter Three:

Growing Up with Anger

My earliest confusion was seeing the frightened looks in my older siblings' eyes when they would take me away from our home, so I would not witness a fight between our parents. There were many times the police would come to our home because the fighting between my parents was so bad that someone, the neighbors or my older siblings, would have to call the police.

My father was always the one to leave, or was told to stop his aggressive behavior. I loved both Mom and Dad and it confused me that love could be so mean. I was twelve years old the first time I saw my father hit my mother. It was not a pretty picture.

As I aged, their anger towards one another became more violent. My mother and father would hurl items at each other and cause bodily harm. It appeared at first that my father's drinking would provoke the fights, but then I began to notice that the drinking didn't start until communication between the two of them fell apart. Mother would become passive and only partially participate with my father's ideas or his endeavors. Anger would overcome him and he would drink. Then he would talk to me about their problems, and at times about the past and things he still held against her or her family. As a twelve-year-old boy, I was told things that most adults should not be told.

My mother and I did not have the close personal relationship that my father and I developed during my relationship with him. As a young boy, I never seemed to have the pleasure of "one-on-one" contact with Mom Raleigh. Because of our larger family, Mom worked outside the household to help support us and the time available with me seemed limited, especially with me being the next to the youngest of the siblings.

Being the youngest son, I recall spending a lot of time with my two older sisters, Doris and Dot. The two of them were given the responsibility of caring for me. They helped me learn to iron clothes, wash floors and windows, sew buttons on shirts, taught me proper manners, and helped me with my homework.

My mother was around the home and busy with the older children. I felt her presence but not like my father's; he was the dominant figure in our family. Whenever I would forget to take the garbage out or failed to shovel the walk, the leather strap was out of the closet and onto the backside of me.

Mother and Dad were strange bedfellows to me. Most of the time they would show open affection towards each other but then sometimes violence between them would happen and those times left scars on my memory and caused me to have nightmares. At thirteen years old, I witnessed a terrible fight between the two of them, and in less than a day, my mother decided to move out of the house and take the rest of the children with her. By this time, my friendship and comfort level had rested firmly with my father. My mother was not absent from the home too long. Apparently, my parents had come to an accord, and she was back living with Dad and I, after just two months of separation. After her return, our relationship became more "businesslike," and we never became friends like my father and I had become.

The triangular relationship of my mother, father, and me became more predominant because of my housing situation. Shortly after being married, my wife became pregnant and to save money, we moved into the basement apartment of my mother and father's home in Fenton.

As I grew and acquired talents as a carpenter and tool and die maker, my relationship with my father nurtured into a wonderful loving bond that seemed to separate me from my mother. They had built many building projects together and I was there to help both of them. During these projects, Mother and I did grow closer. Those times were warm and filled with happy, light- hearted conversation; we rarely spoke of my emotions or hers. We never would discuss heavier topics like politics, religion, and sex.

As I started my apprenticeship in Flint, Michigan, the three of us would ride together to and from work, when I wasn't going to college. Dad and Mom had been working at the same GM plant where I served my tool and die apprenticeship. Their marriage, as I mentioned, was a rollercoaster ride, and the trips to and from our common workplace were a marriage counselor's nightmare, especially if you're the son to both parties.

As the years passed, Dad became more and more ill with his manic-depressive illness and a heart condition, and I became more involved in his life. The polarity between my mother and me became more evident and I was in discord with her regarding some healthcare for my father. I became opinionated that she was the cause of some of Dad's mood swings and his irritability. I disliked that I couldn't share my accomplishments from school and during my apprenticeship with her, or at least it seemed she could not appreciate what I thought was special to me. I witnessed my father's self-improvements during my life through his interest in self-help programs and reading. Yet my mother didn't show the same willingness to improve herself and I grew to resent her for that.

How does this relate to my illness? My father was considered a manic-depressive. Like father, like son? We have a way of duplicating the behaviors of people we admire. He was the best friend I ever had. We could talk and share ideas and not be upset if our ideas were not in agreement. When I was weak, he was strong. When he became weak, I was strong. The relationship between us became more meaningful after he found Lithium, and used it on a regular basis. He stopped drinking and his mood swings became more consistent. Our bond became even stronger when I began my apprenticeship in the tool room where he worked.

My father taught me to witness my own emotions, through Recovery Inc., and use that control to maintain the mood I wanted. Today, I use the lessons from *A Course in Miracles* to spot my thoughts, which enables me to manage my mood swings.

James D. Raleigh, MDP

A Course in Miracles teaches us to look within, for therein lies the answer to anger. The *Course* stresses the total use of unconditional forgiveness to effectively apply the 365 lessons found in its workbook.

My father was confused and he passed some of that confusion on to me. Until I was thirty-six, I was always looking outward to compare my thoughts to an external system of ideas so I could consider myself measured acceptable. The truth lies within me; the external "yardstick" only confused me, and caused much frustration, depression, and a tremendous sense of not belonging.

Why am I manic-depressive? I was forewarned; I was schooled on the behaviors of the monster that is waiting for the slightest change to leap out from the quiet mind and turn that mind into a living hell. I even consulted with my father's psychiatrist several times just before I went off the high dive. He just said that my mood swings into depression were due to the bad economic times. The doctor assured me that things would be okay, so I pushed forward even harder.

I am a survivor of an illness that affects millions of individuals, most of whom are very active and creative people. I am considered fortunate because I can still function on a normal basis and interact with society in a self-sustaining manner. Statistics reveal that only 20 percent of afflicted manic-depressives can lead normal productive lives. I thank my father for a great deal of the patience it requires to continue to educate yourself to the fact that the illness and the stigmas associated with manic-depressive personality are of your own making.

The Lithium that I take on a daily basis, since 1976, only maintains the chemical levels that help prevent a recurrence of mood swings that were not controllable the fourteen major times I was hospitalized for manic-depressive illness. These occurrences most often happened when I was manic/high and not depressed.

The most important concept to remember is not the depression or the mania, but the thoughts that help trigger the escape into these chambers of your mind.

The rapid thought patterns that are allowed to develop by the manic-stricken mind are one of the first clues that a major mood swing is about to occur. The physical changes to the body include the need for less sleep, rapid speech, a rapid occurrence of tasks that are partially finished, rash spending sprees, and sometimes additional intake of drugs or alcohol. The mind appears to become more sharp and creative during these episodes because the speeds of the thoughts are more rapid during the grandiose mood cycles.

My first recollection of a mood swing occurred early in my childhood. Grade school was not difficult for me. During the seventh grade, I became ill with appendicitis and had to leave school for a long period of time. This period in my childhood was lonely. My parents seemed to be gone a lot. My older brothers and sisters were not only my siblings, they were also my caregivers.

When I was hospitalized for appendicitis, both of my parents were in Illinois. I am sure they were notified when I was taken to the hospital, but it was scary to think they wouldn't be there for me when I came out of the operating room. The happy memories of that hospital visit were of the Holy Cross sisters and the female nursing staff that so lovingly removed my fear of being alone.

The time spent at home in the late 1950s for convalescing from an operation was much longer than it is today. I was absent from school for two months. My schoolwork wasn't really that difficult, and I had to study a lot to retain the material being taught. I was a terrible reader, but very good at remembering what I had seen. The homework that was assigned to me was difficult to finish. I struggled through the lessons, however, and returned to school, just barely passing the eighth grade.

My self-esteem was getting pretty low and I recall that I wasn't fitting in socially. The feeling of being lonely was less frightening than being around kids making fun of my stuttering and my pimples. The long period of time I spent at home caused me to feel isolated from my peers. I continued to reason with the idea that my parents were so indifferent regarding my operation. I became resentful and angry towards both my parents and struggled with my self-worth. I felt that they had abandoned me. During my extended stay at home my sister, Janice, who had cancer, was being driven to and from Ann Arbor, Michigan, where, she was receiving Cobalt treatment at the U. of M. Medical Center. My sister, Doris, would drive and I would ride along to have something to do. I recall feelings of separation and aloneness from my parents. Perhaps this is my earliest recollection of my first mood swing, that of depression. I felt very alone and would wonder, "Why I am here? What is my purpose?"

After being away from school for two months, I was apprehensive about returning, because the teaching structure of the small Catholic school I attended in Fenton made you toe the line. The sisters of the Holy Cross were the teachers who taught the Catholic school that I attended. The atmosphere in the school was marshaled. The teaching discipline was maintained with permission to speak only if you raised your hand first. If you were unruly in class, it was not unusual that the nun called you in front of your peers and had you hold out your hand, palm down, as she would strike it with a wooden ruler. In grade school, I was shy and lacked confidence to perform in front of the class. Often, when called on to speak, I became very frustrated and would have memory blackouts just before or during the oral presentations.

The sisters were considerate, but my fellow students made those times nearly devastating for me. I think those times forced me into isolating myself from my peer group. I felt that they had an advantage and could "set me up" and make me feel stupid anytime they wanted. I never considered myself to be in one of the groups that were considered a clique. I had my own "characters" to make me feel included. I could play by myself in any sport, as long as it didn't require a partner.

Recalling the episodes of my early childhood is difficult. The feelings of rejection apparently caused pain and anger. The anger that was denied in my youth stemmed from the frustrations that I felt from the seeming lack of appreciation and love that I didn't receive from my parents. I developed mentors and adult friends that I could relate my achievements to. I felt that my father could relate to my educational improvements and domestic skills. However, if my mother appreciated any of my abilities, she didn't relay that to me. I was reluctant to invite my parents to school functions because they didn't seem to be interested. As I look back during the writing of this book, I realize that much of my high school days were very busy times. I lived in Fenton and attended high school in Flint. During the evening, I worked at a party store and did my chores at home.

With the busy schedule of homework, chores, and working at the little "Johnnie and Eddie" market, it seemed that I would never become socially adept or an educational wizard. However, another side of my personality produced an overachiever, one determined to be noticed because he doesn't feel appreciated.

My first life's dream was to become a priest and help people with their behaviors to obtain happiness. This was partially determined by the unrest I witnessed as a child. The family unrest in our household was common as I mentioned. But Mom and Dad would somehow work things out so they wouldn't have total separation.

As I discovered more about my father's manic-depressive lifestyle, I learned to become an active listener. This happened when I was about fifteen. My relatives and friends were able to talk to me about their problems. I didn't have the solutions and I mostly just let them listen to themselves. Solitude was my method of relaxing, seeking inwardly for the need to be needed by someone.

Being the younger sibling, I watched my brothers and sisters marry and develop their careers and families. It appeared to me that being married established your togetherness and gave you presence in the community. Plus, they seemed happy and I wanted to be happy, too.

My decision to marry when I did wasn't wrong; it just wasn't for the right reasons to maintain a healthy relationship. I didn't question my ability to make marriage work. I wanted to be married for my own stability. I didn't think it was beyond my ability to provide for a family and try to obtain my goal to become a well-educated individual.

At the age of nineteen, I was married, and at twenty, we had our first child. Attending college, working full time, and trying to support my wife and a child resulted in a near-impossible schedule, with no time for me. In retrospect, this is some of the grandiose thinking that is typical of the manic mind. To think that I could do it all and be like a machine was what eventually caused "Humpty Dumpty" to fall. As a couple, my wife and I decided that pursuing my college education should be dropped in favor of food, clothing, and housing expenses. My goal of having a college education had to be put on the back burner.

In the fall of 1964, good fortune came my way. A tool and die apprenticeship at a General Motors facility provided the funding for the college education I wanted so much. This opportunity changed my life and gave me purpose. It wasn't the ideal career path I thought I desired, but it afforded me with the primary tools to get there.

The mood swings that can be completely debilitating were not an issue at this time. But, I was drinking four to six cold beers every day. Somehow, an inexhaustible energy would come over me, allowing me to pace myself and thereby maintain a ten-hour shift at the plant, four hours of class time at college, three times a week, plus study time and family activities. My drinking became a major issue in my late twenties. It was not an unusual occurrence for me to drink all night at a party or a bar after work and then black out, and not realize how I had driven home the next morning.

My anger started to flash into my self-control and take over my behavior. These episodes would sometimes surface during or shortly after a drinking session. Anger was something caused by others and I could blame others in order to justify my behavior.

After some major mental breakdowns and extended therapy, the light finally came on. This anger thing is solely my responsibility. The blame should not have been on anyone. How many minutes, hours, days, and years have I tried to justify my thoughts of self destruction?

The realization that the emotion was my responsibility was not easy to accept. This realization meant that I would have to take a deeper, more insightful look at my behaviors to change the way I perceived the world. What we see inside, we project outside and view it to be there. I thought I had this process under control. After all, my father showed me the secrets of spotting as a teenager, so I was familiar with this seeing within concept.

Apparently, the lessons were not learned well enough. My mind drove my body so hard that it nearly cost me my life more than once. I can give witness to the power of the mind over the body and any other object in this physical world. The ego, which I barely understand, is not a friend of the healthy mind. The manic mind is a sick mind. Confused, it vacillates between right and wrong thinking. The grandiose patterns of the manic behavior, which I have experienced several times, many times overtly aware of this mood, were that the behavior would cause additional delusional energy to support my ego whims.

The other side of the mood vacillation is the sense of *littleness* the ego controls. This results in depression, which complements the ego sense of smallness, or the denial of God's love.

The answer to my lack of self-control was the realization that the source of my anger was within my own mind, but peace was also there. It was up to me to choose anger or peace. Choosing my thoughts determined my external world. The drugs, the therapy, or my choice of environment were just small parts of acquiring the stillness in my mind; the most important process was the choice of my thoughts. We are never apart from our mind and our peace is always with us. How does the racing mind slow itself to rediscover that the answers are already there? We just need to ask the right questions and train the mind to listen, and not wander off before the answer is provided.

Denial is a confusing mental process. I thought it was associated with sacrifice and if I put myself in denial often enough I would receive the love and caring that sacrificing would give me. Actually, my realization of denial came when I woke up over and over again in a deep depression in a back ward of some mental hospital, wondering why I had not been saved from my self-imposed misery. The walls of denial prevented two things — the love I wanted to give away and the love that was trying to help me.

Denial is fear of genuine self-appreciation. It was very difficult for me to get under the many layers of self-hatred of the person that I call "me." Why do we permit this internal turmoil to ruin our lives? The joys of life we deny ourselves can only be reversed by recognizing that conflict is within our minds and not in the world outside.

A quote from *A Course in Miracles* reminds us of this: *Only you can deprive yourself of anything.* Healing begins in the mind. When we stop blaming others, including ourselves, the process begins on a solid foundation. So, some startling interaction with ourselves triggers the need to stop denial and lean into our minds to make better decisions, reduce the conflict, and join ourselves to the joy of peace in our minds that has always been, and will always be.

I experienced a startling event during a manic episode when I was taken into confinement at a Flint hospital. I was strapped to a metal cot because I thought I was Jesus Christ. Believing I was Jesus, I tried and tried to break loose from the cot. My mind decided that I may not be Jesus after all, and instead of being totally frustrated, my mind's perspective convinced me to just be one of Jesus' helpers.

How do I relate denial to this event? I had built an elaborate mental structure around my physical world that prevented love from flowing in all my true relationships. This powerful force of denial caused an episode so strong that my mind convinced my body's interactions not to communicate with family, friends, and the doctors trying to heal me. This was my first trip into the world of physical restraints, which temporarily restrained my body, so my mind could regain control of the monster which had lost control.

Events from 1976 through 1980 are laced with many humiliating realizations that my body has absolutely nothing to do with my peace of mind or my happiness. My yardstick for measuring my happiness had been developed outside of me, being related to the activities of others and how I gauged their behaviors to my own. The many visits to the mental wards and the psychiatric offices made me aware that I was letting the other minds in my life determine my behavior and resulting mood swings.

Chapter Four:

Moodswings and Things

I'm not sure what words would best portray how I overcame the compulsion to depend on the statements and behaviors of others to attain the peace of mind that I now enjoy in relationships. I will share episodes of learning during my times of mania or depression that were relevant to my improvement. Hopefully, you will find them useful.

Abnormal health is an odd concept. In my world of living with a parent who was mentally ill, we would rarely speak or discuss my father's "problem" in public. And if we did, it was in a demeaning manner. However, I noticed quite a difference in the attention that my sister, Janice, received after she was diagnosed with cancer, at the age of fourteen. Her illness was considered a tragedy and my mother and father did everything in their power to prevent her death. I compare these two events in my early life as examples of illnesses that are both life threatening, yet surface on the body and in the world in different ways. Janice, with cancer as the enemy attacking her body, was taken to many specialists to determine exactly what type of cancer she had, and how to treat the parasite that was destroying its host. Friends and family openly shared compassion for such a young lady that had been given a death sentence as such an early age! The special care she received was given without resentment and in the tenderness that hope, faith, and love would provide the comfort she needed to face her body's inevitable death. As I mentioned, I was fourteen when she made her transition, and during the last six months of her life became very close to her spirit.

Illness comes in many forms. In my sister Janice's case, it was physical, but with my father's illness, the form was a mental disorder, manic-depressive illness. My father would literally shield his pain and sickness from his family and hide away until his fears were calm enough to cope with his responsibilities. The different treatment given to the mental patient and the cancer patient is significant to me. The stigmas assigned to ourselves create a sense of separation from society that causes energies about our illnesses to polarize the individual. In my father's situation, little consideration was given to his apparent pain and confusion with an illness that causes massive separation from your self and our families, whereas in Janice's illness and her battle with cancer, it seemed that she was a heroine to be saved from the throes of a common enemy.

I witnessed in my father disassociation from everyone because of the stigmas of his illness. Later in my own life, I placed the same stigmas on myself, but with help, I liberated myself from the effects of the stigmas, which are self-assigned, and can be reassigned. I call this living "beyond the cope."

As I mentioned, my first realization of not being Jesus occurred in Hurley Medical Center, in Flint, Michigan. This was only a stopover on my way to another hospital in Ann Arbor. My wife and family were trying to obtain the best care for me by admitting me to the "Hilton" of mental hospitals: Mercy Wood Neurological Hospital, Ann Arbor, Michigan. During the '70s, it was located in a wooded section of western Ann Arbor with walking trails through the grounds, tennis courts, and several nice seating areas for the patients. The indoor activity rooms were spacious, which included a gymnasium and its own two-lane bowling alley. The staff assisted each individual patient from their private rooms to daily activities that helped the patient regain their social contact. Mercy Wood was the first long term stay I had in a mental hospital. I recall thinking that this is not all that bad, and perhaps I would be able to recover quickly. However, that wasn't the case. Even though, after forty-five days of therapy in a confined environment with adequate rest, controlled activities, and social interplay, on the surface I appeared under control, inside, I was just as frightened and confused as the day I entered this wonderful hospital.

During my first visit to Mercy Wood, I watched one man hang himself. He and I had just eaten breakfast that morning and he told me he was now ready to return to his wife and children, and start his life again.

I was really surprised that afternoon, when a code blue sounded. Attempts to free this man from his closet rod were unsuccessful.

I also met a lady who tried to commit suicide. She had cut her wrists and was in a garage with the car running and the doors shut. Her daughter found her. I asked why, and she explained that because of cancer, one of her breasts had to be removed. Her husband came home drunk one night and said he had been out with a real woman, and had been satisfied.

The lessons learned from this first formal commitment to a mental institution were two — first, take your medicine, and secondly, explain only enough about yourself to get out. Places like this are not for healing; they are holding stations to help determine what you may think you need. In more cases than not, they are also places that allow caregivers to gauge their levels of involvement.

My first wife and I had five children when I first went into a mental institution. My health insurance only allowed a forty-five-day stay, and healed or not, you went out the door. I was stabilized somewhat, but only to the casual observer. As I attempted to work and return to my cycle of living with my family, certain abnormal things would happen due to the effects the Lithium had on my awareness of my surrounding. My co-workers' activities seemed much faster than I could keep up with. It was difficult to follow conversations and to concentrate on the subject matter. It was frightening to involve my mind with present-moment activities of nearly anything; my "focus" was abstract. I was terrified to be a witness to my own activities, let alone responsible for them.

My skill levels before my first manic episode were far above average. Employed as a second shift skilled tradesman at General Motors, and operating a building business as a general contractor during the day, I was considered by my peers to be nearly genius. What a joke. I just set my mind to compartmentalizing nearly every task and delegated nearly everything to someone else. "Organize and then deputize," my father drilled that concept of accomplishing many tasks at the same time.

Returning to the workplace was a lonely, embarrassing experience. There had been an incident inside the tool room where I worked and the police had to be called. Seven policemen carried me from the plant, and after handcuffing me, put me into their squad car. All 6,000 employees at the facility were aware of my situation, or so I thought, when I walked back into the plant after my forty-five-day sick leave.

When I made it into the tool room and waited for my first job assignment from my supervisor, I was shocked when he said, "Jim, you're still on notice. Go to the cafeteria until further notice." My mind went into a state of rage. After all the fears I had overcome to be able to return to work, and now I was being disciplined again!

I was able to continue working; however, after my boss explained that he realized my situation was related to a mental problem, he said that he would let me work through my reprimand. My first weeks back on the job did not go well. The Lithium caused trembling hands, diarrhea, and a gait that resembled that of a toy soldier. My fellow employees were not too kind. They noticed my physical changes and my lack of participation in conversations that required concentration. The paranoia that I experienced was real in my mind and the joking and jeering from my coworkers made me want to become invisible.

These were difficult times, not only mentally, but emotionally and financially. My career was a dual endeavor in order to maintain a cash flow for my family — earnings from the General Motors job, and from my dream career as a builder/general contractor. Apparently, the manic grandiose mood behavior entered into my financial decisions with my business. I was forever "robbing Peter to pay Paul" and under-bidding projects, taking deposit money just to make payments on equipment that I purchased on a "if come" basis which never materialized.

Some major stresses were occurring. My father died, I asked my wife for a divorce, and my financial world was collapsing. My daily activities at work caused my self-esteem to falter. I would perform just on the fringes. I would hide and try to sleep because of the depression I was feeling. Alcohol use re-entered the picture, along with the use of marijuana. I continued pacing my behavior, using the "false powers" of the mania to fuel my body with the energies to ward off the stress I placed upon myself. Sometimes, I would get on a roll and go without sleep for three days. The mass confusion would take over my body and dump me into a heap, much like a wire Slinky that has come undone.

My second visit to the mental ward took place in the spring of 1978. I recall the super calm and feelings of power. My thinking was so clear and quick, my sight reflected images that were so vivid that a third dimension surrounded all objects I saw. The concept of fear wasn't a consideration; it seemed that everything and everyone was in conjunction with me. With a feeling of unlimited power and a feeling of total control of myself and the world I perceived, I dressed myself in a green leisure suit, bell-bottoms included. I was an hourly worker who would not normally be dressed in a suit, so I drew a lot of attention as I walked past the security guard, not revealing my plant badge to him, as I delivered the monthly coffee supplies to my buddies in the tool room at AC Spark Plug. My mood was blissful. I could feel a calm, controlled mind state. I wanted to let my supervisor know that I was taking some time off. That I was okay but I needed to go away for a while. We talked in his office and I unloaded on him like I have never done to any human being. He stayed calm and allowed me to release my feelings.

I felt that a tremendous load was off my mind. My body felt heavy, but good. I remember the song, "Let Your Love Flow," playing on the car radio as I drove home to tell my wife that I was leaving her and that I would be staying at the parish house in Fenton. My wife was shocked to hear what I had said, but stayed composed and packed my suitcases as though I was simply leaving on a business trip.

I felt comfortable when I entered the parish house. The priest seemed somewhat surprised when I boldly stated that I would be staying for the night. To barge into the parish priest house unannounced in our modern society is insane, but that is exactly what I did. This was a major move for me. I had prayed for direction and this seemed to be the correct path to pursue. When recalling episodes like this, anger and confusion flood my mind, as if I am living the moment again, causing me difficulty in recalling the details of what actually did occur. This to me is similar to being in therapy, one on one. I deny my true feeling in my conversations with the therapist because it causes me too much pain to recall the moments that hurt me so much in my past. But, as I learned that sharing my pain and then living through it, I practiced the principles from The *Course*, which teaches us to remember only the loving thoughts from our past. The *Course* further states that "forgiveness is the key to happiness." That made sense, because we can only find God in the quiet of our minds. God cannot be present in an unquiet mind.

The priest and his assistant permitted me to spend the evening and provided accommodations in an upstairs bedroom. They were kind enough to allow me to watch television with them and treated me like I was a guest. I felt right at home and acted just like the priest and I were old friends. As the evening hours came to a close, I excused myself and went to my room.

The following morning, (still manic high) I drove from the parish in Fenton, Michigan, to my sister's home in Parshallville, Michigan. I was feeling an "inspired mood," still thinking that this feeling of power was supposed to be my normal self. My sister welcomed me to her home but was very surprised by my highly elevated awareness of things around me. She spent most of the day listening to me talk about my closeness to God and the feelings of being free from all my responsibilities.

My sister's home is situated near some open land filled with woods and trails. After spending most of the day talking with her, I decided to walk in the countryside and "talk to the animals." My little walk in the woods was most alarming at first. I was able to see deer, pheasants, rabbits, and other small woodland creatures, running as if in slow motion. My right arm was still in a cloth sling because I had chipped my elbow when I fell at work. The arm was healing but I became annoyed with the idea that it had even happened, and because it had not mended completely.

As I was walking into the woods, some thoughts of anger emerged into my awareness and my feelings of utopia changed to frustration. Thoughts of resentment entered into my present moment and my anger turned into a rage that caused me to beat my broken arm into the ground. I was convinced that all the things in my life were totally my fault. After beating on my arm for several minutes, I stopped and felt relieved. I was in no pain, but was exhausted.

I was startled when I looked up and saw my brother-in-law helping me to my feet. I attacked him and tried to hit him in the face with my fist. Fortunately, because of his military training, he knew that he could control the situation, which he did. He was able to talk me down, and led me into the dining room of their home. My sister and her husband controlled me during this manic episode. As I sat visiting with them, I believed that I was the individual who had the situation under control.

When I saw the flashing lights of the ambulance outside my sister's house, I knew I was being taken away. In my mind's eye, I wasn't given enough time to sort things out and heal myself. The mood I was experiencing was so real and vivid. To me, I had plenty of time to reflect and determine what was best for me. But this was not acceptable to society's methods of dealing with individual in trouble and under distress. I was being taken to the hospital instead.

Strapped to the ambulance gurney, I recall the attendant's radio call to the hospital, "Get ready, we got a Jesus coming in from Fenton."

Captivity began. I was told that I was harmful to myself and to others. "We have to put you in confinement until we decide you are thinking right," they said.

Actual captivity is in the mind because no one can restrain the body unless we acknowledge the body as our whole being. There is a quote from an Edgar Allen Poe poem, "stone walls do not a prison make." This phrase explains what is happening in the manic-depressive mind during a confused state. The manic mind to me is similar to the relationship between the ego and the Holy Spirit that is described in *A Course of Miracles*. To reduce the conflict, we can train our minds to think with the Holy Spirit's guidance and regain the peace that is found in the quiet mind. Therefore, we realize that essence of our captivity is of our own making.

My body was put into captivity, obviously due to the fact that I was out of control. I received injections of various drugs into my body in order to enable the doctors to determine exactly how they could help me. Not only was I put in a physical straitjacket, which prevented any freedom of body movement, the chemicals injected into my bloodstream harnessed my thinking ability until a pattern of behavior could be charted to determine what mental disorder with which the psychiatrists could label me.

I will return to explain my activities while spending time with the staff and doctors, but first let me revert back to some of my childhood memories of the manic mind. Perhaps these reflections might change the anger that had controlled my life as an adult and the unstablized life style that fueled my first stages of mania.

A major resentment began to build when I was just a young boy of two. My baby sister was born and her presence in the household replaced my importance. I was told many times at family gatherings that I was very jealous because of the attention she was getting. I think that I adjusted, but do remember the beginning stages of overachieving in order to gain attention from my brothers and sisters, and my parents.

The second major resentment began to fester as more attention had to be given to another sister, Janice, two years my senior, when she became ill with cancer. Janice and I were friends and we shared our fears and joys as young children. We would talk about her dying and the many neat things we had done as kids. I will always remember her telling me when she caught me reading a dirty book, "It's just as bad to read about it as to do it, so just do it." She protected my feelings and she protected me. But when she died two years after being diagnosed with cancer, I was relieved that she was out of pain, but I was also thankful that some attention could now come back to me and my siblings.

Janice's death taught me some important lessons, primarily patience. I changed my school plans to attend high school in Flint, and stayed in Fenton during my freshman year so that I could care for her on my lunch breaks. The second lesson was the faith that Janice demonstrated just before she died. I think that is when I realized God works through all of us. The relationship that Janice and I developed as she struggled to breathe was not of this world. My resentment was present, but it was hidden in a loving relationship between a brother and sister struggling to live.

The year I spent attending Fenton High School was very difficult for me. I literally missed more days than I attended. The "C" average I maintained barely got me admitted into Holy Redeemer High School. My mother had to persuade the principal to allow me to take an entrance exam before she would admit me. I was on probation my sophomore year. If fear produces anger, then that first year at Redeemer certainly made me angry.

I surprised myself by making the honor roll the second semester. I would study in the mornings before attending classes, and I would study in the evenings. To improve my reading and handwriting abilities, my father insisted that I copy one article a night from *The Flint Journal*, the daily newspaper, and present it to him for approval. I continued to develop better study habits and expanded my social world at school. I was very surprised, when in the latter portion of my junior year in high school; the principal approached me to be the yearbook editor. I agreed.

Doing so provided me with my first taste of college. Holy Redeemer paid for a two-week training session for yearbook editors at the University of Detroit. I stayed at the dormitory and attended classes. I was impressed. At that time, the ideas kept returning that I should attempt to enter the seminary and become a priest. This made sense to me. I was always told that I had a calling. The family members always seemed to share their deep dark secrets with me and I would listen with forgiving patience.

My father, however, discouraged me from not only the seminary but also from attending college. The most disappointing moment came when the principal of Holy Redeemer said I must have cheated through high school because my grade point average was much higher than my IQ justified. She refused to complete my applications to the seminaries that had requested transcripts.

The initial fears of entering a high school that made me a probationary student for a year had been surmounted. I had made the honor roll and even became the yearbook editor. However, these accomplishments were not enough for me to win the support of my father to go to college. As a result, the fear was now a hidden rage. I was determined to make college somehow; I knew I was well worth the effort.

My social life was beginning to improve. I always felt that I had some special appeal that attracted girls, but I felt uncomfortable in their presence. My female cousins and I had several close emotional relationships that permitted me to experience some physical awareness of the opposite sex. Dancing was one social endeavor that I adapted to quickly as a teenager, but my general social skills were lacking. I felt at a major disadvantage when trying to maintain even a simple conversation. Small talk was not among my God-given talents.

The transition from an introverted pimple-faced kid to a young adult willing to assume the leadership position in any business or social setting is interesting. The focus required to nurture myself came from many determined moments of introspection guided by my father, teachers and social contacts. The lessons I learned were not easy, but without them, my life would not be fulfilled. "A quiet mind is not an idle gift," (ACIM) and oddly enough we always are at peace, we just are not aware that we are. There are no sacrifices required, just the realization of a higher power, or source, within. But why did I continue to seek outside of myself for the peace that was waiting to be accepted within? I was studying my effects instead of being aware of my true Self, the real peace within me.

My efforts as a child to become less petrified of speaking in public were witnessed during my efforts to read the Epistle and Gospel reading during our Sunday Masses at our parish. I volunteered to read in order to challenge myself to read before a group of people. I would practice the pronunciations of words that meant nothing to me, and play my readings back on a reel-to-reel Webcor tape player. I was so terrified that once, during the readings, I left the speaker's platform and went to the sanctuary to get a glass of water, which took about three minutes, and then returned to complete the reading. The priest was fuming! I was never scheduled to read again.

To expand my horizons and improve social skills in a group setting, I joined the Young Christian Students at Holy Redeemer High School. This informal group setting allowed me to share some ideas in a less intimidating atmosphere. It seemed that ad-lib conversation without social order was most difficult for me. To be in competitive conversation, or thinking on my feet, caused me to panic and shut down my awareness. I was very fearful of not being responsive quickly enough, and I would either act dumb or mumble an inaudible response, pretending not to be interested in the subject matter being discussed.

My high school sweetheart was to become my wife the first year after our graduation from high school, and I was still determined to follow my dream of obtaining a college education. Our first child came just nine months after our wedding. Fortunately, I had started my tool and die apprenticeship, which to me was my ticket to a higher education. The apprenticeship not only provided extra income from the skilled trades wages, but the college courses provided for technical studies as well as speech, math, and English courses. This delighted me and enabled me to become more adapted to public speaking and convey my thoughts in social conversations without embarrassment.

Our marriage was being blessed with a child every twelve months or less, and by the time we were twenty-three, we had three youngsters still in diapers. The apprenticeship was a blessing, too, but between ten-hour shifts at the plant, college four nights a week, time spent with my wife and children were limited. I think these years launched my ego into high gear regarding my self-importance. I lost focus of the real meaning of a relationship and of forgiveness. My youthful drinking habits gave way to supportive adult problems that justified an extra beer to solve the unhappiness in this busy marriage and fatherhood. I was becoming an overachiever at college and at work. My fellow apprentices would ask for help with their projects and I would relish the fact that they asked and I was able to help. I also became more active among the general workforce of the plant. These activities fueled my eagerness to perform, regardless of the cost to my overall health.

We have a tendency to model the people we admire. Interaction that occurs in various social settings cannot help but affect our behavior. The interaction between my father and me contributed to some of my manic-depressive behavior. I was indirectly involved with his illness as a youth. Our relationship continued into adulthood and into my apprenticeship arena. He was a journeyman in the same tool room that provided for my training as an apprentice. As I became a senior apprentice and more politically involved in the workplace, I was informed that my father had a reputation of being very moody and boisterous sometimes.

The rocky relationship between my parents carried over into my adult life and surfaced during the most unusual circumstances. The three of us worked in the same factory and it was convenient for us to commute to work together. But it also put me in the middle of a relationship that had implanted some harsh memories from my childhood that I was trying to forget. Both parents were more than supportive of my career and marriage. My problem was trying to balance the act of being "marriage counselor" to them while still maintaining neutrality as their son.

The plant floor is no place to play counselor to your manic-depressive father and maintain good progress reports with your supervisor. Our conversation would become much too involved and sometimes his marriage situation would become entangled with our relationship as father and son. I was under pressure to listen to him and tried to unravel his concerns, but I knew I should stay neutral. Our relationship never ceased to be loving and forgiving. He was a soul mate who I could share my thoughts with, even though the thoughts would gnaw, dig, and scratch within my mind.

My father's flamboyant personality, piggybacked with his manic-depressive illness, was a major influence on my sense of being. I gauged my behavior on his approval until his death. As a young man, I admired his determination to investigate his mood swings and his winning personality in gathering individuals together to discuss their problems. I admired his moments of insight, which permitted his warm and loving side to bless his wife and children. It was difficult because he had been such a mean and unforgiving father, and sometimes a rude and physically aggressive man towards my mother in the presence of his children.

I knew both sides of this monster I called friend and Dad. He was kind enough to give me some examples of what to do and not to do. How is the bipolar personality formed? And does the lack of Lithium unleash the monster activity? We parrot our parents, but if we are strong enough, we undo that mimicking activity and challenge the mold we think is ours. My father influenced me so much that I feel his presence within and around me constantly.

I continued with my apprenticeship and was considered above average by my peer group. During my apprenticeship, my father was aiding my older siblings with some house building projects. This was the start of my building career. I would help my brother and my father on various construction projects. I became very familiar with the processes involved in constructing a house, from the basement to the roof. This involved hands-on participation, so all the skills required to operate the various tools became second nature to me.

Dad was usually the coordinator of these projects until he became ill. He developed a heart condition and the undetermined mood swings of his manic illness caused confusion during the completion of the projects. My resentment began to build when this would happen.

His first major heart condition produced a blood clot in his neck that required surgery. This was a very apprehensive time for all of us children, especially, for it was then I realized he was mortal and I was resentful that my good friend was no longer available to me. The surgical procedure required that his heart be stopped for a short while, in order to remove the blockage. The surgery was a partial success, but I feel his brain was affected and this complicated his mood swings.

My memories of many visits to hospitals to be with my father, through his physical and mental problems, are difficult to recall. The most vivid visits were after he had been given shock treatments to try and remove some bad memories from his brain. During the 1970s, this type of shock treatment was standard procedure at the time to help cure manic-depressive behavior. The mental ward where these shock treatments were performed is the same hospital ward I was taken to during my first state of mania.

These episodes with my father made me become aware of the devastating effects an illness has on both the patient and caregiver. Despite his treatment of my mother on many occasions, she stayed devoted to my father through all of his illnesses. I became involved as a caregiver and a marriage counselor as his physical and mental illness caused him to make some very bad financial decisions. Mother would attempt to talk with him and persuade him to wait and discuss things with my brothers or me, but many times it was too late. He became very dependent and childlike before he came to live with me and my wife, just prior to his death in 1978. He trusted me and loved to spend time doing minor chores for my brothers and me in our new building business.

Two years before my father's death, my first manic episode started to unravel the story that is contained in this book. As I write this, I am beginning to realize the stress levels that I was maintaining, believing that I was a machine instead of a mind that could control its thoughts to maintain a healthier body.

Chapter Five:

The Unraveling Begins

In pursuit of my dream to shine for my ego, my brothers and I started a building company in 1973, with me serving as the president. We were most capable of performing the multiple tasks for completing houses; the trick was securing the proper building contracts with adequate budgets to make a profit for our new company. My wife understood my determined efforts to start this new business venture.

Once again, my father was an issue in my decision. He practically begged me not to leave my secure skilled trade job at General Motors. His lack of support added fear to my decision to leave the security of my job, but my grandiose, flippant attitude gave me the false power to make the decision to leave the security of my job. I quit General Motors, leaving all the security of regular employment and medical benefits behind me. I was twenty-seven years old at the time and I thought I was sitting on top of the world.

My wife was supportive, as were my brothers, and the economy at the time seemed rosy. There were many building projects available for our new company. I started educating myself on the legal aspects of the construction business by attending college classes in the evening, studying real estate and construction codes. The responsibilities of running the business, meeting with clients, subcontractors, suppliers, building inspectors, and giving estimates, nearly eliminated my quality time with my family.

Pressures began to mount regarding our agreement to provide ourselves with weekly wages. I felt my two brothers wanted a regular, forty-hour check each week regardless of the income received from our building projects, and I could not guarantee that to them. The red ink, however, continued to spread across our business books. A sense of guilt hung heavy in my mind because my plans of success were beginning to be dark with clouds of doubt. I kept the budget overruns from my wife and brothers and worked harder at quoting new projects. By accepting more remodeling projects, I could demand advance monies to start the work and then use the new cash flow to handle the payroll and other overhead expenses. However, the end result was a lack of funds to complete the individual projects because the money had already been spent.

A staggering event occurred in the latter part of 1974. My wife's behavior was changing and I asked several times if she was feeling sick. A month or so passed and I finally said, "You know, I think you're pregnant." She was tested and sure enough, our fifth child was born. Fortunately, we had maintained our health insurance with General Motors. But things were not going according to plan. Prior to leaving General Motors to start the construction business, my wife and I agreed that I would have a vasectomy. We agreed that four children were enough, so this new addition to our family came upon us like a brick balloon.

I began to drink more and found release from my problems in the bars, with my neighborhood friends, strange women, and music. I always loved to dance and this temptation resulted in a one-night romance that changed my life and marriage. The sordid details are not important, but returning home late that evening (or morning, I should say; it was 4 A.M.), my wife greeted me at the door, determined to make me confess what I had been doing all evening. After much questioning, I could not lie and shouted back that I had slept with another woman. I realized that our marriage was doomed from that day forward.

During the remaining three years of our marriage, there were many missed attempts at repairing a relationship that was filled with mistrust, of a broken business venture, and the ravenous effects of my manic mind that caused poor perceptions, resulting in bad decisions prior to my first admission to a mental hospital.

Regardless of our shaky marriage, we continued to finish a four-bedroom house that we started in a rural setting in eastern Michigan, with the anticipation of using it as a model to spur new home projects and to provide the living space for our growing family.

We completed the home on a shoestring budget just before Christmas of 1975. Eight months later, we had to sell the house to forgo a personal bankruptcy. Our business experienced a shortage of new projects and next-to-zero cash flow. My brothers and I cosigned on a loan to put money back into the business. The loan was just enough to keep the creditors away for six months. In the winter of 1975, we stopped accepting contracts because no building activity was available. We decided to seek employment elsewhere, and were able to find work at Excel Corporation in Fenton.

The three of us continued to work through the winter months, but I was planning to seek out new building contracts to repay the money we had borrowed from the bank and continue in business with my two brothers. But when I approached them with the idea, both said they wanted nothing more to do with the business and said they were going to continue working at the shop. They said it was up to me to figure out what to do with the business. I felt abandoned and the pressure of resolving the business problems by myself caused me to lose sleep. I felt guilty for putting my brothers into debt. I began to drink more heavily.

My marriage was continuing to slide downhill, and the income that was required to maintain the extra mortgage payments for the business debt provided a perfect opening for my wife to seek employment outside the home. I fought with her about the fact that our children, in my opinion, needed their mother around the home more than we needed the additional income. I presented an itemized listing of the expenses related to her work, including car, day care, clothing, and meals. The expenses exceeded her weekly income, yet she insisted on starting to work. The feelings of being inadequate caused me more guilt. I was a poor husband, father, and business partner.

James D. Raleigh, MDP

The following events are like a blur in my memory. In an effort to protect our children's health situation, I went back to work at General Motors in order to obtain medical health benefits. This move provided the income and the time for the unraveling of my manic mind. Even though my re-employment was at a different location, the feelings and failure and depression would rain down on me each time I rang the time clock. I felt I had failed my father, brothers, children, and my wife. My wife objected to filing both personal and business bankruptcy. Her lack of cooperation caused more separation in our relationship. Conflicts concerning our children, social lives, financial matters, and our sexual incompatibility just seemed to become more and more prevalent at that time in 1975.

Determined to make things right, I removed the business activities from our household, rented space in a commercial building, hired a secretary, and without the support of my brothers or my wife, began to recreate the building business, while continuing my career as a tool and die maker with General Motors. These were very lonely and fearful times. I was concerned with my father's health. When both of my parents moved into our house, it increased the stress in our marriage. My recent changes in business location increased my sales, however, and the business was again becoming successful. My self-confidence was beginning to grow. This juggling of time between jobs did not leave me time though to devote to mending my broken marriage or spending time with my children.

My mother's presence in our household was very helpful as she babysat for our children, especially the two youngest. My wife's new job outside the home provided extra income, but increased the friction in our marriage. It caused major problems regarding our quality time together. Her career pursuits during the day and my business activities and second-shift job didn't make for a honeymoon situation. She became more and more distant from me, and my interests. Some of the lonely evenings at the shop produced insanely jealous illusions of her and her bosses together having fun and purposely excluding me from their activities.

Moving the business from our house into the public eye had proved to be a good decision. I used the family name to run free advertisements in a local newspaper concerning a hometown boy returning to his roots to start a new business. Friends of the family were supportive and the referrals increased business activities. Advertisements were pictured showing me as the "idea man" for remodeling projects. The young secretary proved to be of great assistance. Together, we established an office procedure to handle the increased flow of new homes and remodeling projects. The old business debt was still hanging over my head, but the new cash flow was forestalling the inevitable bankruptcy of my personal debts and that of the corporation.

I was aware of the mood swings of my manic mind and discussed them with my father's doctors during visits with my father to try and maintain *his* emotional stability. When I went to my father's doctor with my concerns and related to him the stress levels in both my business and marriage, he commented that several businesses were having difficulties and said I should just be calm and ride out the storm. The last time I visited his office, I recalled the deep lonely feeling of despair, that sense that my last hope for guidance had led me to nowhere.

Suicide had crossed my mind several times; the expressway abutments that support the overpasses seemed to be calling my name. I would think that all my worries would be over if I just ran the car into the concrete pillars and let the insurance take care of the whole damned mess. After finishing a typical business day — 6 A.M.: Hit the floor running and do as much as possible until 1 P.M., shower, eat dinner and be at the clock to start another shift — I felt like an empty shell waiting for my public image to begin unraveling like a big ball of string.

The night shift provided a reclusive world that protected me from several external stresses. The discomfort of my relationship with my spouse was making our conversations very superficial. The meaty, meaningful dialogue with my coworkers provided me with an outlet to support my ego and autonomy, which I was destroying so effectively during the daylight hours in the public arena of the business world.

Unknowingly, this outside world of confusion was only in my mind. But the mind is the determinate of our world and the perspective that we view is one generated only by choices. Obviously, this little bit of insight comes after twenty-five years of painful searching and untold numbers of wrong choices. One huge wrong choice was the idea that all of the suffering of the loss of a marriage, a father's death, and a business taken into bankruptcy was my fault, and consequently, all the guilt had to be projected onto this inner self who I didn't really like in the first place.

The idea of suicide did, in fact, cross my mind and one might easily understand why. The confused state of mind is exemplified to yet another level considering the mood swings of a manic individual.

Until the fall of 1975, I had not had a grandiose high. The extra energy and insight into my thought patterns, which I now recall were not as erratic and sensational as that month of October. Somehow, the timing was just right for the release that I was about to experience. The floodgates of emotions were firing from my inner being and rocketing into my mind, searching for direction. I couldn't stand the excitement. My nights and days flowed together into one continuous flow of feeling powerful and all knowing. The illusion that I was Jesus only appeared in my mind, but it felt real to my body. The actions that I performed never really left the inner chambers of my deeply confused mind.

Chapter Six:

Putting Humpty Dumpty Together Again

"All the king's horses and all the king's men ..."

These lines are familiar to most Americans and are from a nursery rhyme that depicts an egg that is knocked from a wall, and can never be reassembled, no matter how hard the king and his people try. I used this fairy tale in a talk I presented to a group of skilled trades journeyman in my facilitors training classes at General Motors in the Flint area. The idea of using the small plastic egg-shaped containers that panty hose are sold in struck me as a good way to demonstrate to my fellow trainees what a person's mind is like after a major mental illness has happened to them. I placed four candy corn kernels in sixteen plastic eggs, to represent the four sides of my personality. During my presentation, I used on overhead projector to cast images of my main character, Humpty Dumpty, sitting on a brick wall. I explained to my fellow skilled tradesmen that I had fallen off the wall during my mental breakdown, and that the broken pieces of Humpty's egg were how I felt during my recovery. I changed the slide and cast an image of a garbage can with Humpty and his sad face. The slide also showed written words like loneliness, worry, fear, anger, and depression. I passed the eggs to the individuals listening to my correlation of Humpty, and his fall to my fall, from sanity to insanity; I explained, as my doctor had explained to me, that my mind was like someone had taken my brains, put them into a garbage can, and shook the can, and then handed it back to me, saying, "This is your life to straighten out." I then asked my fellow trainees to open their eggs. I explained that each candy corn represented to me the four sides of our personalities.

As the group examined the pieces of candy, I changed to the next overhead that showed a rectangle and an oval in the center labeled

ME. The four sides of the rectangle in my slide presentation were labeled: Social, Mental, Physical, and Spiritual. It was explained to me during my first hospital stay that if we, as individuals, maintain a fair amount of balance in these areas of our daily living, that our sense of self-worth will be able to nurture our mind and body towards a balanced personality. It can also help prevent recurring mood swings, or worse, a major mental breakdown.

I depicted how I slowly developed more confidence in each area. When I felt insecure in the social arena because of paranoia, which sometimes troubles me today, I would go to the spiritual or physical side to help make me more balanced. Sometimes, I would work on the mental side too hard and put myself into a self-defeating frame of mind.

This formula for bringing one out of total disorientation seems very easy to apply for someone who has been through the turmoil of a manic high or a severe depression resulting from extreme physical exhaustion. As I write this chapter about putting One's self back together again, I remember how desperately I held onto the grandiose feeling of relaying the "fact that I was a disciple of Christ." I had tried to convince my doctors how important these feelings were to me, that I was in control, and I had been given the answers.

To apply the principles of the four-sided rectangle, you must first be aware that you have choices in deciding which side best suits your moods while you are positioning yourself for a balanced personality. I was so drugged and confused about me that it took nearly four years of intense self-study to effectively decide which side I needed to move to when and how to do so.

First and foremost, my feeling of insecurity was overwhelming. Many times, I didn't feel worthy of treatment, but somehow a "voice" kept repeating that if I would only lead with love, my fears would be removed. It assured me I could maintain a healthy enough behavior to be released from the chains that my self-made fears had created from childhood.

A book that opened a path for me early in my recovering process is *Love Is Letting Go of Fear,* by Gerald Jampolsky. The format and suggested lessons for re-establishing the love of self that is God-given are outlined in a simple manner that affords the reader salvation from anger that hampers so many of us. Forgiveness is the central theme of this little book that saved my life and allowed me to trust in God's guidance.

Four years of struggle was really a short amount of time when considering the hell I was making for myself. The manic mind is controllable because the mind controls everything. The working mechanisms of the physical brain are the monsters that must be harnessed. For me, these are controlled in part by my daily intake of Lithium. When the brain is in a state of frenzy, it is very difficult for the mind to control the mania or depression it's confronted with.

Chemical control came as a major shock to my system and caused difficulty in applying the four-sided rule of thumb for stability. The realization that the mind could control my behavior came when I would only take the Lithium during periods of hospitalization. Once released, I would stop taking the Lithium in order to regain the grandiose feelings I thought should be normal for me. This routine continued for two to three years, until once, while recovering from an overdose of Lithium, I had mixed alcohol and marijuana at the same time. I landed in the back ward of a Flint hospital, lying on a simple canvas cot. A doctor, who was not assigned to my case, but had seen me come and go from the "psycho ward" at the hospital, simply said to me, "When are you going to stop feeling sorry for yourself and stop your foolish game?"

That doctor's straight talk provided me with the incentive to move forward and leave the merry-go-round of my "poor me" life behind. This comment was made to me while I was waiting to be transferred from Hurley Medical Center, Flint, Michigan, to Ypsilanti's mental health facility.

These visits to Ypsilanti had become routine to me as I had been admitted nine times prior to this last admission. Hearing the comment from the doctor at Hurley served as a wake-up call. During my last stay in Ypsilanti, I monitored my behavior while I was on the open ward that houses both men and women. The routine forty-five days of insurance coverage was coming to an end and I knew that I was to be discharged shortly. The attendants came to me a couple of days before my stay was to end and explained that I was being transferred from a co-ed ward to an all-male ward. I was angered that this was happening.

When I initially entered the ward, apparently I appeared to be agitated and I walked to a bulletin board that was on the wall and ripped a small piece of paper from the cork board. Shortly thereafter, I was told to remove my shoes, belt and any other loose garment because I was being taken to a padded time-out cell due to my disturbing behavior. I didn't resist the lockup, but after being in a seven-by-seven-by-fourteen-foot-high padded cell without toilet provisions for more than four hours, I simply urinated all over the floor and continued singing until the attendants opened the door.

The two weeks I spent on this ward were the worst I can remember. The rules were very strict and control over the phones and other social activities was very limited. Once, when all of us men were acting out of control and being unreasonable, the entire ward was given a 200-mg dose of liquid Thorazine to control our activity. This happened on more than one occasion. The head nurse reminded me of the way the staff handled the patients in the movie *One Flew over the Cuckoo Nest*. We, as patients, were so marshaled and herded about; I surely didn't witness much healing during the last visit at Ypsilanti.

The game playing continued between the staff and the patients until I became more aware than the others that I could beat the staff at its own game. I became self-assured on my last admittance. My girlfriends would visit and bring cigarettes and other gifts. Being enterprising, I would sell the cigarettes for five cents each to my fellow patients, allowing me to have spending money at the little store inside the hospital.

My last discharge from Ypsilanti was in 1979, but I was not allowed to go out on the street immediately. I was taken to another hospital in Flint, Michigan for observation by another psychiatrist. This observation was to determine if my behaviors reflected a state of control which would permit me to be released to the streets. The doctor and I had instant rapport with each other and after two days of testing and observations, I was released to enjoy my freedom.

My father died in September 1977, after my first trip to the psychiatric hospital. My mother and I were never close. I think my personality reminded her of my father's and she resented me for that. While I was in the hospital, she did visit me a couple of times. Christmas Eve, 1978, I was on the second floor of Hurley Medical Center in Flint. I recall how frightened I felt to be dressed in white hospital garb, very drugged, and so out of place. I was embarrassed, but comforted that my mother and younger sister, Catherine, were on the ward with me. The hospital had a Christmas tree, and patients and caregivers sat around a long table and sang Christmas carols. I recall that it was during that same Christmas that I was allowed to leave the ward to visit my five children at their home. My ex-wife was kind enough to sign me out of Hurley so I could share Christmas with the children. I returned to the hospital very frightened and lonely, and feeling guilty about nearly everything. My mother's visit was a very reassuring moment in my recovery. Shortly after that, she gave me enough money to make my first security deposit on a one-bedroom flat in Flint, about a half-mile from where I was employed. This gave me a new beginning.

My budget was very tight. The $225 per week child support represented 50 percent of my take-home pay, and the rent took about a quarter of the remaining money. With car payments to take care of as well, what was left was very little for starting a new life. My income was adequate when overtime at the factory was available, but when forty hours hit home, disaster was the name of the game. I continued with group therapy, but after two to three months of the same people telling the same loser stories about why they could not get better or move on with their lives, I picked up Humpty Dumpty's pieces and left for the social world again. The group interaction helped both social and mentally, however, the continued negativity from the personalities in the mental health support group was causing me more blocks to my awareness than improving them.

A Course in Miracles encourages us to live in the present moment, the *now*, and to let the past go and only remember the forgiving thoughts from our past. The *Course* also teaches us that we should not deny the past, but acknowledge the pain and through forgiveness, release all attachment of its effects. With the guidance of gifted therapists, group therapy, Lithium, *A Course in Miracles,* and accepting true forgiveness, I have begun to understand the problematic life of a manic-depressive person.

Manic is a mood, moods are emotions, and a painful mood is hard to remember. Who likes pain, even it is only in your mind? Your mind is all you really have and the confused manic mind is really in pain, perpetual pain. *A Course in Miracles* teaches that the mind, when producing a thought, changes the world in some manner. Illness is of the mind, the *Course* continues, and the thoughts we generate are manifested in our bodies or onto someone else.

The pain that I felt was real. It caused me to make decisions that affected my life and the lives of people who loved me. It also affected my attitude toward everyone and everything in this world that I call home. The split mind of the manic is described well in the Course. In our minds is the presence of two thought systems, one is represented by the Holy Spirit, the other is the ego. Our true Self, if chosen to determine the thoughts we make our world into will eventual provide us with a quiet and peaceful world. The ego is a thought system, which is present in our minds, that has been built on fear and if we chose to side with it consistently we will witness a fearful world. Regardless of our physical condition, these thought systems stay alive in our split minds. My mind finally stopped its whirling and confusing movements between the two thought systems, one of love and the other of fear, when I regularly chose the Holy Spirit in my decision-making process. *A Course in Miracles* has provided the path of stability for me as I move "beyond the cope" and live in a more loveable world.

During the initial intake process when I was hospitalized, police, or security guards, restrained me with handcuffs because I was considered a danger to myself and a danger to others. Once, while being admitted to the mental health ward of a Flint hospital, I was sedated with a needle and my body was placed in a cloth straitjacket. I remember coming out of the sedation and looking up; I saw steel bars across a small window. As I peered upward from a cell floor, that was no larger than seven feet wide by twelve feet long, I could feel the second straitjacket come free, while a staff member allowed my right arm free from the restraint. This movement allowed me to feed myself from a metal food tray that had been placed in front of me.

My body was so out of control that it had to be restrained to calm all the resentment and anger that was being projected from my "unquiet" mind. This mania lasted two to three days, during which time all of my meals were delivered through the opening at the bottom of the cell door.

The chemicals that were given to me during my unstable times altered my mood swings, but were not the answer to my anger; they just allowed me to cope. The manic-depressive personality must gain control of its decision maker, which is in its mind, to provide the answer to its conflict. The realization, that you have a problematic disease that will never be cured, is very frightening. No human wants to live with the idea they must be dependent on another mind, or several other minds, to control their behavior.

To heal myself with right-minded thinking, which to many, like me, means choosing the Holy Spirit to make my decisions, is difficult when the body is suffering such turmoil. The caged animal treatment was necessary to shock and still my body so the stillness of my mind could be recognized for its power.

A manic mind is a sick, insane monster that thinks it has unlimited powers and takes no enemies along its quest to satisfy whatever goal it wants. A manic-depressive individual may be determined to be a good or bad person. Adolph Hitler was considered very evil and he was manic-depressive. On the other hand, Theodore Roosevelt, Abraham Lincoln, and Dwight Eisenhower were considered very honorable and good citizens. Here is a limited list of famous individuals that are manic-depressive personalities: Jane Pauley, Robin Williams, Edgar Allen Poe, Ted Turner, Kurt Cobain, Winston Churchill, Jim Hendrix, Janis Joplin, Robert Bly, and the list continues. Thousands of individuals have been struck with the disease of manic-depressive illness and they have risen above the torment that the mind experiences to bless the world with fruitful endeavors. However, the mind does subject itself to a living hell while providing the blessings witnessed by the world!

We can all relate to the rage the manic feels. This rage is sometimes uncontrollable, and sometimes the results are very harmful. I was fortunate that the harm I caused was limited to the shame and embarrassment to my family.

My controls were taken from me. I chose to let myself be controlled because the stress on my body caused a physical exhaustion that resulted in several major hospital confinements. The straitjackets and the drugs, having an attendant shave me; episodes like these are easy to remember.

Through these memoirs comes the love the friends, family and hospital staff members gave to me. My hospitalization usually took place after I had physically exhausted myself. My manic highs would drop me into confusion and depression. To give highly detailed examples of the treatment I received would be very sketchy, and the purpose would not give credit to the hundreds of nurses and doctors who helped care for me. The love that I felt in their strong, firm touch and in their eyes, sometimes filled with fear (but always compassion), helped me to slowly regain the self-esteem required to believe that I could stay calm enough to heal myself of this mental illness.

The process I used to become less dependent on the chemicals first began when I decided to let Lithium truly work on my body. I stopped drinking alcohol for a year while continuing to attend group therapy. The difficult adjustment was the social interaction I felt when my family and friends noticed I was not drinking. The paranoia was paramount. They seemed to know that I was not only unable to control my thoughts because I am manic, but now they knew I could not control my drinking. As my habits of drinking and doing some mild street drugs reduced and eventually diminished to nothing, my circle of friends changed and the members of my mental health group became my central focus of relating to people.

As nearly two years passed, I started to get frustrated with the group. The members seemed to talk about the same problems over and over again. They sounded like a broken record, repeating the same issues again and again. They didn't really want to get back into the real world, I thought. They were all talk, and no action. To me the group was just coping, talking in circles about their problems and causing more confusion, rather than offering solutions and support.

It was 1980. With new independence, a place to live (and run to when scared or hurt), I began to build a new character with the pieces of my personality that were still salvageable. I am still building; I have discovered that nothing changes. Only love is constant. With my fellow workers more than aware of my problems, I was supported in several ways. They became like family to me. They listened to my concerns and I listened to theirs.

My background as a builder also provided me with knowledge that was of interest and help to many of my coworkers. The networking that occurred on the factory floor gave me several opportunities to bid on side jobs, which gave me extra income to support my slim budget. This interaction allowed my self-confidence to grow and let another side of the magic rectangle to experience some nurturing.

My family time with my children was still lacking, but with my new apartment, I could at least have them over for the weekend and take them to a movie, skating, or some other activity. Another social activity that came into my life during this period was the continuation of my college education. General Motors' policy of providing tuition refunds paved the way for me to attend the University of Michigan-Flint for a degree in engineering. The exposure to the young students on campus stimulated my interest in improving my life. I spent extra time in the library and took advantage of the music learning facilities, as well as the indoor pool and jogging track. These activities proved to be what "Humpty" needed to refill his shell with the defenses required to maintain a happy balance between the four sides of our personalities.

As my new character grew more confident, he began to realize that *giving is getting*, as opposed to *getting is having*. The love that I discovered within myself could not help but come out. I know that I hurt people and that people were frightened of me, especially when I would go manic high. So the "old character" gave the "new character" a very bad rap even before he had a chance. Rather than explain away the past of the old character, I set forth to demonstrate that the new character indeed had forgiven the old character, and that he could start anew, despite the damage that might have been done.

First and foremost: with blame, there is no gain. In healing myself, I took full responsibility for everything that ever happened to me, which may have affected anyone. With these words, I released my little self to my inner Self, affording the kernel of light within me to grow and glow more brightly in my new character. During this period of my restructuring, I remember reading some works by Jonathon Livingston Seagull and the strong implication to be independent, almost to the point of being in total solitude to find inner peace. However, through studying *Love Is Letting Go of Fear*, I realized that there was another way of find myself. Finding yourself in your brother without peace, we know not God, but with sharing our inner peace we can recognize that we are thoughts of God.

This relates to the manic activity in several ways. Once anxiety of the manic mind is forgiven, awareness enters the picture and accurate feedback can be utilized to maintain a "new character," much like Humpty Dumpty did in my little story. The patient must realize that he or she cannot depend on any outside forces to maintain this balance. The chemicals used to control the mood swings are for the brain only, not the mind. You control your choices, and your proactive choices are independent of the chemicals. We are aware of millions of individuals who depend on chemicals for various illnesses. More often than not, these chemicals cause the patient to become limited in regards to their cure because of the coping mode that becomes apparent when healing is not accomplished over a long period of time.

The four years that I was attempting to heal myself were filled with this pattern of coping. I felt very stable and nearly ready to reach out and touch the brass ring, but the limits of coping would restrict my efforts and my self-confidence would diminish. It was if a voice inside my head was telling me, "You could try for the ring and you might even get it, but you really don't deserve it, anyway, so why try? Just *cope* and be happy."

The fear to overcome coping (which apparently was preventing me from truly discovering the joys of appreciating the "new inner Self" that I had denied) was a very trying ordeal. I recall the many times that depression would cause me to go in a full circle, just doing a simple task such as going to my job. Now that I understand the depression and how to avoid total immobilization of my body functions, I have decided that since Humpty acquired all these rebuilt defense mechanisms, he could shed some more egg off his face and return to the "real world" and not be frightened that his shell would fall apart again.

Benefits of utilizing the four-sided rectangle was my saving grace. As a youth, I depended on someone outside of me to gauge my behavior and reward me accordingly. Since this method of appraising did not prove to be successful, I was given another guide to allow me to serve me in appraising my decisions and subsequent behavior. My personality "rectangle" was my yardstick and if the balance was maintained, I enjoyed joy and peace through each new shaky venture.

As an example of how I was able to utilize the holistic personality model. I returned to college and exercised my mental side, and while I was at school I began more social because of the interaction with the instructors and the students. The Flint U of M campus had just built a new physical fitness center, with an indoor swimming pool, a racket ball court, and many other indoor workout facilities. I joined using my student admission rate. The physical side of my personality was more than complimented by this activity, and again the social side was enhanced. As I mentioned the *Course* was and is my central focus of my spiritual side. As I became more confident my security of my nucleus inside my rectangle, I began to attend my church and spiritual group meetings to complete the four sides of my personality. With awareness of my thoughts easier to control I would overtly start conversations about my manic-depressive stigmas and exchange all four sides of my personality on a daily basis. For instances while I was in college I would share my social, physical, spiritual, or mental activities with someone in a conversation and it would permit other sides of me to be exposed to the individual and allow a "safe" sense of networking with each other and in the same moment developing a more balanced inner core for me.

The continued use of this model I call the "holistic person" has helped maintain my manic highs and lows since I was last hospitalized in 1979. My Lithium provides the chemicals I require to restore my brains need of lithium, but if I want to enjoy life and be consistent in my creativity, joy, and happiness then I must extend the effort to use the model and experience the joy of my manic-depressive personality.

The following are the overhead projector slides I used during my presentation.

Humpty Dumpty takes a great fall

And all the King's horses

And all the King's men

Can't put Humpty Dumpty

Back together again.

Humpty falls from his sense of wholeness.

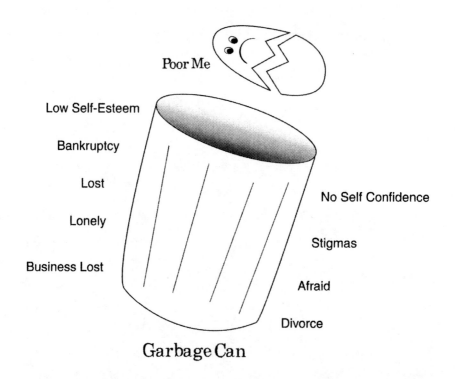

Poor Me

Low Self-Esteem

Bankruptcy

Lost

No Self Confidence

Lonely

Stigmas

Business Lost

Afraid

Divorce

Garbage Can

"Your brains are like someone has put them in a garbage can- shook them up, handed them back to you and said- This is your life."

Dr. Erol Ucer, 1978

Humpty is in great need of repair.

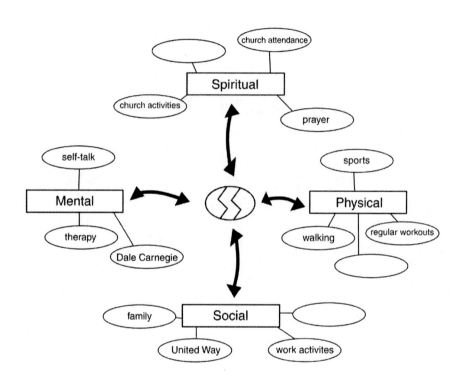

Humpty Dumpty putting the pieces back together.

__Humpty puts his pieces back together, to become whole again.__

Holistic Person

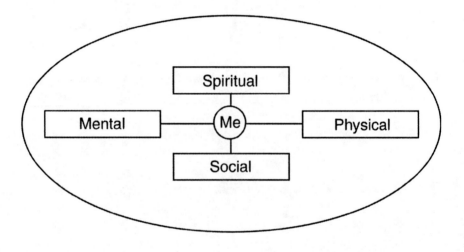

__Humpty's wholeness, using the four sides of his personality.__

Chapter Seven:

Benefits of a Mental Illness Stigma

Beyond coping is the rebuilt defense mechanism that gave me the freedom to discover my new self. Roughly two years after my total explosion into the manic-depressive mood swings that gorged my inner being into small fragments, I was able to move into a one-bedroom flat. With me went the precious few belongings from my marriage. If I recall, the only piece of furniture that belonged to me in the apartment was a custom-made birch veneer desk that I had made for my father.

Thanks to the tuition refund program at General Motors, I was able to enroll in a clinical psychology course at the University of Michigan, in order to begin studying my depression and learn how to control my mood swings in a more objective manner.

Midway into the clinical psychology course, the class began discussing the term "stigma" and how it related to the various mental illnesses that were distinguished by the consistent body language of the mental patients. I asked the instructor if he had ever heard of someone using their known stigmas to their advantage. The instructor asked me what I meant and to explain my intentions. I said that I was manic-depressive and that I was going to tell the world that I was manic and proud of it. The instructor said, "Try it and let me know how it works out."

The results have been outstanding. The idea wasn't easy to put into practice at first; I feared that my ego would not be able to take the ridicule and rejection when I would mention my stigma to others — especially at dinner parties and other social get-togethers. The more I injected the idea into conversations, the more I realized that it was a subject that frightens a major part of society.

Usually, I would allow the conversations to flow naturally until the subject of a social disorder would come up. The relationship of the body to mind is nearly impossible to avoid in any conversation. It seems we are continually trying to motivate and control that relationship. This imbalance is magnified in the manic-personality to a point of "spiking behavior," much like a Doctor Jekyll and Mr. Hyde. So, introducing my illness induced many conversations that permitted a perfect stranger to shed his or her own "eggshells" and relate his or her mood swings and behaviors. The release of my stigmas through these open conversations allowed me to come to an understanding that many individuals were experiencing the same discomfort that I was witnessing. The only difference was that I *realized* my imbalance and had been educated on controlling my behaviors, whereas they would not maintain theirs. I believe the disclosure of my stigma propelled me to a new level of understanding.

The declaration of my stigma was not to my benefit, however, when it came to my career. I was limited from being promoted and was considered a high risk when asked to assume leadership roles that required quick decisions. "Raleigh's just a walking time bomb." I would hear this comment often when my name came up regarding a leadership role. But the personal conversations I had with my managers would often lead to their mental instabilities. Through my declarations of how the Lithium would provide a stable mood swing, the managers would let their walls down and share how they were handling their depression, insecurities, or family issues on a personal level. In honesty, the GM managers admitted, my career at GM would have improved if I had not broadcast my mental illness.

My promotion to tool room supervisor in 1982 was the height of my career at AC Spark Plug, a Division of General Motors Corporation, Flint, Michigan. Oddly enough, the tool room I was assigned to supervise was the same tool room where I experienced my first mental episode. The promotion came after about four years of rehabilitation work, supported by my family, friends, co-workers, and management of the General Motors Corporation. During this time, GM created a program for troubled employees. It was a cooperative program with the UAW and GM to reduce employee absenteeism. The several sick leaves I took to help stabilize my manias and depressive states qualified me for the program. I was reluctant to participate at first, but then realized the benefits were rewarding and would help me keep my job with GM.

Becoming a supervisor was a career goal I had aspired to since I first started my tool and die apprenticeship. My ego wanted to prove that I was as good as my older brother. I wanted to shine in my father's eyes. My technical background as a tool and die maker gave me the right of passage, and my experience as a building project manager gave me the experience to maintain schedules, to complete the construction of the tooling in a timely fashion. I was directly responsible for building new progressive dies and maintaining the "up time" of several production press operations. This allowed me to use my "spotting techniques" in maintaining a sense of balance amongst the twenty employees assigned to my department.

At first, I was very nervous. The foreman training me was the same supervisor I had when I was going through various stages of my mental illness, and during that timeframe, he took very serious disciplinary action against me. Flashbacks, for me, were common and the uncontrolled fear would cause me to experience panic attacks. My mind would go blank and I would feel the "flight or fight" syndrome. I was able to train my mind to stay focused on the issues being discussed and ignore the conflicting memories that caused me uncertainty. God only knows how I was able to maintain my outward appearance of calm and control, because inside my mind, it was chaos. The love that kept coming through me gave me more determination to stay calm during these episodes, and let the situation resolve itself.

Some unkind situations came courtesy of my fellow workers. I was promoted from within the same ranks I was now supervising. Various articles published in the local newspaper regarding mental illnesses were cut out and left on my desk. Several written suggestions were also left on my desk stating that I should resign my position. "You're crazy to think you can be a skilled trades supervisor" was among the comments written in grease pencil across the articles concerning mental illness. Regardless of the battering from a few small-minded individuals, the majority of skilled trades employees I supervised respected my leadership, and I was very successful in maintaining the production floor schedules, and I met all the deadlines for the new tooling we were producing.

I had a new wife at this time. The support I received from Frankie during this difficult time was extremely helpful. Frankie had managed a women's clothing store for more than twenty-three years. She shared many techniques in dealing with the management of personnel. I refused to let my self-esteem be diminished by the ridicule of the employees I supervised. Instead, I would go to the various sides of my personality to support these moments and realized that the accusations were more from their insecurities than mine. I have had to constantly remind myself that I am the only one who can intimidate me, and the many moments of insecurities I was exposed to during this career opportunity gave me plenty of opportunity to do this.

My career as a supervisor ended because of a major reduction during the automotive industry recession of 1987. Because I was a per diem employee as a supervisor, I was permitted to return to my hourly skilled trade position as a die maker. During this demotion, I utilized the principles of the "magic rectangle." The reduction from supervisor to hourly worker caused some significant financial concerns. Frankie and I had just started our first new house together in Mundy Township, Michigan, and my income was reduced by about $400 a month. General Motors' management had already committed verbally that I was to be made a permanent salaried employee, and we had prepared our budget accordingly. When I was abruptly informed that I was returning to the bench, I became very angry and my self-esteem, along with my ego, was damaged. I took a vow at that time never to trust the income from GM and pursued by general contracting career with fervor.

It seemed like a very long time before I could forgive the GM management for their decision. My mind would not accept the idea that because I was manic-depressive, GM would not promote me to a supervisory position.

I realized that this thought was damaging my productivity as an employee and was spilling over into my marriage and other personal relationships. It also caused me to return to alcohol. I didn't recognize the cause of the effects of these thoughts, so I started the cycles of denial and increased my dependence on inhibitors to cover the feelings of failure. I was able to spot this self-defeating process and accepted the idea that something else bigger and better was in store for me. I let go of the resentment and decided to utilize my talents in my own general contracting business.

This decision allowed full synergy to be employed and I turned to a trusted old friend. George was a lifelong friend who was very helpful to me in my career as a builder. He and I served our apprenticeships together at a General Motors facility. His background was in automotive mechanics and mine was carpentry. Our friendship was good from the beginning; we trusted each other. He was a Nazarene and I was Catholic, but I think he was more intent on his spiritual path than I was on mine. George was considered a bit of an outcast among the other apprentices, but for some reason, he and I shared many in-depth conversations about various subjects, ranging from politics to building houses and racecars, the latter being his favorite subject. He knew everything about cars, inside and out. We grew to be very close friends and business associates.

George had a young, growing family, and on several occasions he would hire me to construct various projects for their house. Once, I designed and built a complete set of kitchen cabinets using birch-veneered plywood. After completing the kitchen, George said, "Jim, you know the only difference between an amateur and a professional is that an amateur does things for free, but a professional does it for money." That comment started my professional career as a builder.

After my demotion at General Motors, I approached George again. He was serving on the board of directors at a Nazarene church in Flint. I called him to talk about some building projects again. To my surprise and delight, he was happy that I was getting back into the building business because he knew it was my first love.

The board of his church had decided to expand and agreed to meet with me and discuss some structural designs for a new building. I explored the possibility of using a geodesic style of dome building being distributed through a company in Davison, Michigan. The phone call to my friend George, and the willingness of his board of directors, catapulted my career. The East Flint Church of the Nazarene contracted my new company to construct this new building style on their site. I went forward with this concept and designed and built six new church building at various locations in the state of Michigan. My part-time career as a general contractor expanded into the field of consulting. I performed study plans for building committees and individual homeowners.

I stayed very active in my business until Frankie realized that something major was malfunctioning with her body.

Chapter Eight:

Hope in a Second Marriage

My recovery progressed forward as I gradually put "Humpty Dumpty" back together again.

Using the magic rectangle, I started to gain self-confidence in the dating game. My spending money was very sparse due to child support payments, thus leaving very little money to entertain my five children, or to spend dating new women.

In 1980, I joined an organization called Parents without Partners (PWP) to seek female companionship and provide an outlet for my children. This group provided family activities for single parents with children. The interaction helped my children realize they were not the only kids dealing with the trauma of divorce. The club offered many activities during the special holidays, as well as weekend camping trips, and field trips to various entertainment parks. The many dances at PWP allowed men and women to socialize, and of course, dance.

My first extended relationship lasted for about a year. I was interested in meeting a woman who would help me raise my children. The lady in my first relationship was not ready for that task. We broke it off and I started to become more involved with the PWP organization itself. I was elected to the board of directors and was assigned to form a subgroup for widows and widowers. I named the group "Movin' On." The board decided that the group should be formed because of the relationship difference between single divorced parents and the parent who is widowed. As the facilitator of the group, I gained much insight into the differences of trying to reconnect. There is a vast difference in dealing with the death of a spouse versus a divorce.

I attended hundreds of dances in the basement of the yellow brick building at Third and Garland, in downtown Flint. The speakeasy-type entrance down the basement stairs always made me think of the Roaring Twenties. It cost only two dollars to get into the dances, and guests were allowed to bring their own alcoholic beverages. I joined the club to meet a new mate and I was always on the lookout for new members.

One evening, in January of 1982, I noticed a slender, curly haired lady come out of the ladies' restroom. I had never seen her at the dances before. I waited until an opportunity presented itself and asked her to dance. To my surprise, when I introduced myself, she said she had never met me before, but knew of me from Holy Redeemer High School. She said she was a junior when I was a senior and had noticed me. She also said she knew some of my background, including being married to my first wife, who she also knew in school.

As we danced, I shared with Frankie that I was now divorced and had been hospitalized for mental illness. I also told her I was working second shift at AC Spark Plug in Flint and had to pay $225 a week in child support payments, and would she still like to keep dancing? We continued to dance and our conversation flowed very easily. She seemed to know more about me than I knew about myself. After our dance together, we returned to our respective tables.

As a director of Parents without Partners and being known as a man who liked to dance, I was busy visiting with other people. Then, I noticed that Frankie had left the dance before I had a chance to get her phone number. If the meaning of "thunderbolt" means that you are stopped in your tracks upon meeting someone of the opposite sex, then I was indeed hit with a fantastic bolt of lightning!

Fortunately, while we were dancing, Frankie had mentioned that she was the manager of a certain clothing store in Flint. The following morning, I looked up the number and called the store, convincing the manager of another store in the same chain that I must contact Frankie. The manager violated management rules and gave me the number of the store Frankie managed.

Frankie was reluctant to date me, but as we shared conversations, I discovered that she was selling some bulldog puppies. I purchased one of the puppies just so I could visit her at her house. God's love started to connect us together and we realized that the relationship was good for both of us. We agreed to stop attending PWP dances because we considered our bond of love very special, and to continue attending single gatherings would send a mixed message to the individuals we respected.

Frankie's situation wasn't much better than mine. She was beginning single parenthood. She and her son had to take on a female boarder in order to help with the monthly bills. I made sure Frankie was aware of my manic-depressive illness and the effects that it would have on my behavior. She accepted me as I was. We agreed it would benefit both of us if I moved into her home and paid her rent instead of continuing to do so with my own apartment. The arrangement worked well until the lady tenant's boyfriend came to pick her up for a date and saw me at the house. Shortly thereafter, the lady moved out and it was just Frankie, her son, and I living in the home. We became a more involved unit and a family atmosphere developed. Frankie's former husband was a typical father, in as much as he was concerned for his son's health and safety, with a new man living in the same home with his son. He was intruding at first, until he realized I had his son's best interest at heart.

More than a year passed, and Frankie and I were most assuredly in love. I asked her to marry me and she said no. She explained that it was because she wanted someone who could take care of her if something was to go wrong. Shortly thereafter, I moved my things out of her house, while her son was crying and begging me not to leave. I contacted my mother before making the decision to move and she said I could stay at her rental home in Fenton.

While staying in Fenton at my mother's home, a phone call from Frankie made my spirit spring to life. She wanted to come and talk with me about our future together. This meeting came after only two weeks of separation.

We married on February 17, 1984. The fact that Frankie accepted *me*: my personality as a manic-depressive, my five children who came with the package, and then, agreed to my proposal of marriage, demonstrates that God's love works in many wonderful ways.

Frankie and I accomplished many things in this material world in a short time together as husband and wife. But more importantly, our love gave each of us the strength to provide a haven for our children to nourish God's love in themselves.

After battling Mylona cancer, Frankie left this world on April 24, 2000. God's love allowed us to help her be patient through three stem cell transplants, which helped to keep life in her body for three more years, after discovering her stage four cancer in 1997. Frankie's understanding of God's love, with infinite patience, permitted additional research data to be gained about stem cell transplants, which may help future recipients.

As mentioned in this book as well as is stated in *Manic-Depressive Illness,* the exact cause that triggers the disease in our bodies in not known. However, stress is claimed to be one of the major factors in the release of the monster within our minds. Without the help of my daily Lithium and the tools I learned from practicing the *Course* and the balance I receive from utilizing the holistic personality model I have described, I know that the stress I experienced during Frankie's cancer ordeal would have put be into back a mental hospital.

I have not remarried and am still searching for a partner who will allow me to experience the fullness of me and still be together with her. The holy relationship that the *Course* speaks of is possible while living in this illusionary world. I feel that the realization of that relationship is witnessed every time I allow the spirit of the person in my presence to be "seen."

Mania is a state of awareness that enables the individual to be more attuned to "seeing" and I feel that the manic-depressive personality is gifted in many aspects because of this. The dark shadows of the disease discount the individuals who get beyond the cope by various means.

The stigmas that are associated with manic-depressive illness are becoming more acceptable in a society that is beginning to embrace individuals who are attempting to be responsible. In healing our minds, we become responsible to our true Self, not our personality. Stigmas are the sandbags that make the illusions seem real. These stigmas are truly self-inflicted; the journey within permits all the bags to be emptied from the effects on the Self.

In the *Course,* Jesus shares the true meaning of forgiveness. Without this understanding, I would not have been able to accept the gift of loss of Janice's death, Frankie's death, or the continued challenge of living with a manic-depressive illness.

After realizing that my cure is within me, loss took on a new meaning. There is no loss, only gain. The gain is the realization that your happiness, joy and peace are within you. The animal that was tranquilized and put into a straitjacket wasn't me, any more than the things that my body did wrong or right were me. They just happened on my journey home — home to my Self, the One who has no end and had no beginning.

The manic-depressive personality is a gift to the world. It has been my wake-up-call to the real me. To say that the manic-depressive is a stigmatic problem is not to realize that gifts come wrapped in various packages. Try to be patient with yourself and take a moment to look within yourself…the gifts are waiting!

Peace,
Jim

Printed in the United States
61720LVS00002B/82-180

9 781420 889321